PHILIP GROSS
Off Road to Everywhere

PHILIP GROSS was born in the small slate-quarrying
village of Delabole in Cornwall, the son of a wartime
refugee from Estonia and the village schoolmaster's
daughter. One of his poems for adults opens 'I was the
son of the Duke of Nowhere . . .' He started writing
poems and novels for young people after his daughter and
son were born, and has visited hundreds of schools,
reading his work and leading writing workshops. Now he
is Professor of Creative Writing at Glamorgan
University in the mining valleys of South Wales.

JONATHAN GROSS spent his formative years in Bristol,
matured in Cornwall, and now lives with his wife and son
deep in the nooks and crannies of mid Wales. He studied
Illustration at Falmouth College of Arts, and in 2006 he
was shortlisted for the Times Canongate *Life of Pi*
Competition. This is the first time he has illustrated
writing by his father Philip.

Also by Philip Gross

for Anne

PHILIP GROSS

Off Road
to Everywhere

Illustrated by Jonathan Gross

CHILDREN'S POETRY LIBRARY
No. I

LONDON

PUBLISHED BY SALT PUBLISHING
Fourth Floor, 2 Tavistock Place, Bloomsbury,
London WC1H 9RA United Kingdom

First published 2010

Printed in the UK by the MPG Books Group

Typeset in Oneleigh 11 / 14

ISBN 978 1 84471 722 4 paperback

1 3 5 7 9 8 6 4 2

For Jacob Ioan David Gross
and John Karl Gross,
great grandson, great grandfather . . .

. . . and for everyone in every class or course or workshop
who has played these games with me.
These poems are only a part of it.

CONTENTS

ACKNOWLEDGEMENTS

'White Ones' and 'Old Nanny Neverley' first appeared in *Wicked Poems*, ed. Roger McGough. Macmillan, 2004; 'The Living Room' in *Michael Rosen's A–Z: The Best Children's Poetry from Agard to Zephaniah*, ed. M. Rosen, Puffin, 2009.

CAMPER VAN DREAMING

On the windows are stickers and flags
from everywhere:

from Florida to Loch Ness,
from Sun City to the Mountains of the Moon

and some that can't be true

(*Drongoolia? The Gulf of Zunch?*)
and parking tickets and

I ♥ any old thing
(*Skydiving? Goats? Bear-baiting? School?*)

on the windscreen that you can't see through.

The rainbow paint is flaking, hubcaps rusted
and the tyres are flat.

The door
squeals open — *crump*, falls off its hinges.

There are voices, laughter. 'Climb aboard!'

they call. There's a party in there.
'We're just about to leave.'

Where for?
'Off-road to everywhere! You'll see . . .

The last place on earth still unexplored.'

WHITE ONES

With small scritchety claws
and pink
shortsighted blink-
ing-in-the-sunlight
eyes that looked raw
as if they'd cried all night . . .

One morning they were gone.

On holiday,
says Dad. *Gone to stay*
with their friends
in the pet shop. And so I pretend
I don't know about the cage door
he left open. I try to ignore

the look on the face of the cat.

It isn't that
wakes me up in the darkness. No,
it's the scritch and the scratch
at the bars, those pink-eyed
lies. They're only little
white ones, oh

but watch them breed and grow.

3

DREAMS OF AN INLAND
LIGHTHOUSE-KEEPER

ON THE BOAT MADE OF WIND

The hold is laden
    with scents you can't name,
a hint of other weathers, and the itch
        of desert sand, and bells, and butterflies,
        and voices out of lives and cities
          we can see but never touch,
        because this is the boat made of wind,
        and all we can do, we see-through crew,
        is fly. We have to fly.

~

THE BAD SHIP ANACONDA

has the soul of snakes
    just like its fork-tongued captain.
      It cuts through the waves with a hiss
or lies at anchor, every porthole
    watching like a stone eye. Then
      it strikes — part dagger-thrust, part kiss.

Or it swallows you whole,
     down through timbers that ripple
      and twist around you, squeeze, crush,
grind you to a paste, a powder
     that the captain primes his guns with,
      silent cannons that pound: *Hush. Hush. Hush.*

~

THE BOAT MADE OF SUSPICION

     whispers over the waves.
The weather is doubtful. So are the shifty-eyed crew.
     All night the lighthouse
gives its knowing wink. The gulls shriek with laughter
     as if there was something they knew
and won't let on. The boat might be not what it seems.
     Might be no more than a twitch
of the eyelids in somebody else's dreams.
     And so might you.

~

THE BOAT MADE OF TEARS

is little different from the sea it floats on
— salty, with strange tides and currents,
both flow as and when they will.
        But, if you find yourself of board,
            don't be afraid. You'll never sink.
At worst, you'll melt into the whole
wide world around you — like the ocean,
wild and gentle, always moving, always still.

∽

THE BOAT MADE OF HAIR

stands in the garden of the barber's shop.
He has been building it for years
with the sweepings-up from all his customers,
black, white, ginger and grey.
He plaits them into tiny ropes, then hawsers.
Nothing, he knows, is as strong.
                                One day
his ship will launch itself, through rain and spray,
onto the high seas, and you'll see him
on deck, cutting straight for the horizon,
away from this greying old back street

where it's glum blokes' heads,
not sails, he has to trim.

∾

THE BOAT OF PURE MATHEMATICS

needs no engine, no power, only
          calculation, like a gull's flight
straight down the line of its gaze
          at the battering storm
that could pummel it into the waves.
          The gull hangs, quivering, calm, calm
              as the cross-hairs of a rifle sight.

∾

THE BOAT BUILT ON STILTS

is posh-particular,
          almost too well-bred to touch
the common water.
          My grandmother used to eat
new-fangled food she wasn't sure of
          with (she said) *long teeth*.

So this boat twitches over the world
        like a pond skater, wincing
when the slick pool's surface
        puckers,
        sucks and clings
to the touch of its delicate feet.

∾

ON THE BOAT MADE OF SECOND THOUGHTS

the crew keep gazing homewards
        (even the steersman)
        as if, oh,
each of them had dropped something
        overboard — maybe his heart,
        his soul —
as if he could still see it, bobbing
        in the wake, or paddling off,
        the way
rats do, who've seen what's coming
        and jumped ship
and they never look back to say why.

∾

THE BOAT MADE OF STARDUST

. . . from another world
might be ordinary dust in ours.
Pity the poor sailors
    plunged down cracks in sofas,
    hacking through rug-thickets
    hung with cobweb drift-nets,
under floorboards in an netherworld of mould.

No good now, their magic powers,
no *with-one-mighty-bound-they-were-free*.
No such luck.
        But the tales to be told:

    dust-devils dancing round them
    in the whirlwind of the hoover,
    the clang of a flip-top dungeon
then the screech and grinding of the bin-man's
truck . . .

and if ever one gets back to write the history
of their shipwreck on the dreadful shores
of Ordinary . . .
        well, who'd believe him?

∽

THE BOAT MADE OF POEMS

sings and hums and talks and whispers to itself.
    It never sleeps.
It groans, it shudders to the rhythm of the waves.
    Its timbers creak
in the language of every port it has put into —
    the backchat, the patois,
the babble, the Babel, the smuggled rich lingo
    of each dockside bar.
But hush: don't tell the captain or the bosun
    or the loosely rhyming crew:
        there's really nothing to it, poetry,
just air, hot air and paper, oh, and skill
    and love and hope, between them
        and the deep dark silent sea.

HIDE

at Loe Pool, Cornwall

Oh the hard of the stone and the soft of the rain,
the new of the green and the old of the grey,
the wrapped-up-and-snug of the might-have-been,
the huddle and shiver of here today . . .

  Eaves drip with slow
  at the pool of Loe
as the lowdown evening slinks away.

Oh the null of the view from the birders' hide,
the SHARON 4 GARY and worse on the wall,
the been-here-and-seen-it-before of thirteen,
the heartache by numbers in blue feltpen scrawl . . .

  Spring aches with grow
  as the pool of Loe
downloads its seasons' rise and fall

Oh the sharp of the swallow's flick out of the mist,
the blunt of the pencil, the smudge of the word,
the fact that I'm writing this poem at all,
the still-and-for-always of once-seen-once-heard . . .

The sky below
the pool of Loe
reflects on something that's occurred.

It's the yes of the no
in the hide of the show:
the twitch of the moment, or was it a bird?

for Roger Butts

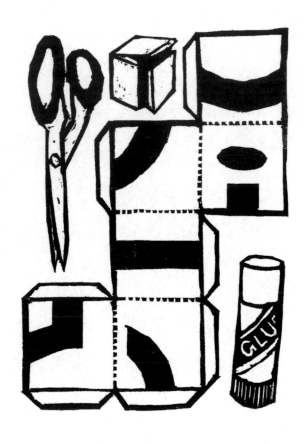

LEFT LUGGAGE FROM THE LOST AND FOUND

Item: one crate of raw planks
nailed together, weather-worn,
sea-bitten, washed up. Flotsam or jetsam.
How long has it kept afloat, to come to me?
Inside . . .

> you'll find a sudden stillness,
> the reflection of the harbour light
> and laughter on the water, one last evening.
> Calm before the storm. We sail tonight.

~

Item: seems to be a strongbox,
dented metal, strapped and braced —
not one right angle or one straight edge —
beaten out of shape by life but never burst.
Inside . . .

> if you could ever find the key
> you'd find a brittle powder-blue
> blown bird's egg, and a note beginning
> *Dear, I found this, and I thought of you . . .*

~

Item: a box of mirrors.
Every way I hold it, the same face
stares back — now grinning, now puzzled,
now frowning, now blushing, now terribly pale.
Inside . . .

      who knows? What's so precious
      or toxic that it needs such high security,
      so many masked attendants, never
      sleeping — these massed ranks of *me*?

THE GOPHER'S TALE
*(gopher: builder's junior assistant,
always being told to 'go for' this or that)*

He sent out for 15-amp fuses.
He sent out for pizzas and glue,
     some inflammable gunk
     that said Not To Be Drunk.
He said Save me the dregs if you do.

He sent out for chrome-plated handles
and candles and vandal-proof paint
     and extendable legs
     and hard-boiled eggs.
He sent out to file a complaint.

     *And I went, I went
     when he sent, he sent,*
He might have been some sort of saint.

He sent out for prickly-pear yogurt.
He sent out for porpoise and chips.
     He sent out for gyres
     and tricycle tyres
and half-bricks and hamsters and whips.

He sent out for Lonely-Heart pages
and chisels to carve a reply.
     He sent for a peach
     and said Get us one each
and whatever you do, don't ask why.

     And I went, I went
     when he sent, he sent,
because well, he was that sort of guy.

He sent out for something surprising.
He sent out for three hearty cheers,
     a lathe-turner's bench
     and a back-handed wrench.
He sent out for twenty one years.

He sent out to ask what was happening
in Ecuador, Bath and Tibet.
     He sent a demand
     saying Don't Understand.
He sent out to place a small bet.

     And I went, I went
     when he sent, he sent.
Wouldn't you? There was so much to get.

And he never once came to the window.
He never once came to the door
   and the last time he sent
   Heaven knows what he meant
but he never came out any more,
       any more,
   though I knocked and I rang
   and I called and I banged
no, he never came out any more.

TAKE A CITY

Take a city, any city.
See it as a map of light . . .

all-night dusk
    dull orange sky
flightpaths winking
    five miles high

connections flicker
    made and broken
nonstop chatshow
    words unspoken

backstreets smoulder
    rubber burns
hot night joy rides
    handbrake turns

thirteenth floor
    one square of light
a single pixel
    in a sign that might
be signaling two words:
    'alone'
      'tonight'

Take a city, any city.
What you see's not what you get.
Under the surface, dreams and secrets,
dark fish tangled in the net.

Take a city, any city.
See it as a score of sound . . .

Machine-made hush-hush
        heartbeat hum
bypass throbbing
        muffled drum

a dog barks   sudden
        threat or fear
at nothing we can
        see or hear

a car alarm
        cries on alone
blue lights flicker
        red light zone

a rub-a-dub thud
        from a passing car
a whiff of Kingston
        Ja-mai-ca

going going going
       gone
        too far
Take a city, any city.
What you hear's not all you sense.
Here we are together — it's a wonder
of the world, this vast coincidence.

Take a city, take this city.
Listen when it speaks to you.

Do you take this city
to be your lawful wedded home?
            I do.

A million other voices answer,
one by one:
            I do.
             I do.
              I do.

PETRA AND THE WOLF

It's dark. You've called,
you've called. Is anyone there?
The babysitter's got the TV on
a hundred miles downstairs.
    You told Mum: 'Promise,
    tell her that she's *got*
    to leave the landing light on.'
    Yes, dear, yes. And what
      did they do? It's dark,
      dark. One of them forgot.

A line of moonlight
slants in up the wall.
The shadow of your hand becomes . . .
A dog? Up close, it's small.
    Sharp ears, sharp nose, sharp eye.
    Look, you can make it grow.
    Move your hand, it gets bigger
    and bigger and worse . . . No!
      Hide your hand. But what's
      that quiet *Oh, o-oh . . . ?*

A small sad howling.
'Who's that?' *Set me free.*
'But who?' *You've heard
of crying wolf. That's me.*

Put out your hand.
I won't bite. Do you dare?
I don't eat girls, just shadows.
Well, you've got shadows to spare.
    Thank you! Now, come
    with me. 'Where?' *Anywhere!*

Run! You're both running
four feet and two
over long fields of snow
bluish-white, whitish-blue.
    Then ice: a frozen lake.
    And you look down
    on streets and roofs,
    a sunken town,
        and silver bubbles rising
        like souls of the drowned.

Run! through forests of dark
chilled as brittle as glass
where thin icicles shiver
and chime as you pass.
    Don't look back, till
    on a hilltop stone
    you lie side by side
    and pant. But . . . 'Don't

you get lonely,'
you say, 'here alone?'

He lifts his head,
O-oh . . . 'Don't cry.'
No-oh . . . It echoes
faint and high
    all round you:
    wolves, and still
    more wolves. They sing
    across the chill
        pale miles of tundra
        hill to hill.

From pack to pack
across the flickering
Aurora sky, to the Pole,
to the stars, they sing
    one song: *No . . . Not alone.*
    And there you are
    till you look back
    and down and far
        away there's a moving
        light, a car

that you know. *Run!*
says Shadowolf. And all
his running-brothers,
whisper-sisters, pour
 down the valleyside
 like dark smoke blown
 downhill; keeping pace
 they race like shadows thrown
  by headlights in the trees
  as they carry you home.

It's dark.
Downstairs in the hall
there's Mum's voice:
Did she sleep? Did she call?
 Oh, the landing light's off . . .
 'Not a sound. I'd have heard.'
 You tuck down tight.
 When she peeps, you won't stir.
  And Shadowolf? Oh,
  he won't breathe a word.

PHILIP GROSS

AMELIA'S LUNCH

with thanks to W.S.Graham

The railway steps into the sky
held by girders and struts
in silhouette against the grey
cloud-flow. An early leaf
falls, jiggling slowly

to the road a hundred feet
below, as Amelia dangles
her feet and swings them,
her petal-pink lunch box beside her
and many birds singing.

It is an ordinary day on which
nobody has looked up
from the road and seen her.
no one started waving arms
and running to and fro

as she picks out carefully
the lettuce her mother
has to slip in every
sandwich because it is good
for her. She lets it drop.

The railway steps into the sky
held by girders and struts
in silhouette against the grey
cloud-flow. An early leaf
falls, jiggling slowly.

NANNY NEVERLEY

Old Nanny Neverley
came from Back There.
She sat in the sunshine
with frost in her hair.
I'm going home soon, she said.
Never said where.

Sweet crumbly biscuits,
ghostly-grey tea
and a smile would be waiting.
She listened to me
and sometimes to someone else
I couldn't see

and when we fell silent
and couldn't say why
she glanced at the window.
She smiled at the sky.
Look, there, you missed it.
An angel went by.

It was one of her stories,
like: *I'm growing too;*
you grow up, I grow down . . .

She told lies, I knew.
Only, now that she's gone
nothing else seems quite true.

MASTER MÖBIUS PRESENTS . . .

(A shape easily made from a strip of paper, twisted once, which in theory only has one side, the Möbius Strip was allegedly discovered by two mathematicians at the same time, unknown to each other, one of whom was August Möbius.)

Blank   page
dull   day
blunt   school
scissors   snip
a long thin strip

> just   think
> what   if
> end to end
> a single twist
> and stick

this side that and thick side thin
welcome to the world turned outside in

take a pencil
walk the line
until you reach
the opposite
a one way trip

to the other side
from down to up
(but upside down)
from here to there
from flop to flip

off side on and dark side bright
welcome to the world turned wrong side right

and where you go
is where you've gone
infinity
a DIY
time slip

and what is where
and who is which
the universe
has dropped a stitch
but Master Möbius
has picked it up
here it is at
your finger tips

my side yours and your side mine
ours and theirs and hers and his
welcome to the world
welcome to the world
    (there's no two ways about it folks
      that's just the way it is)

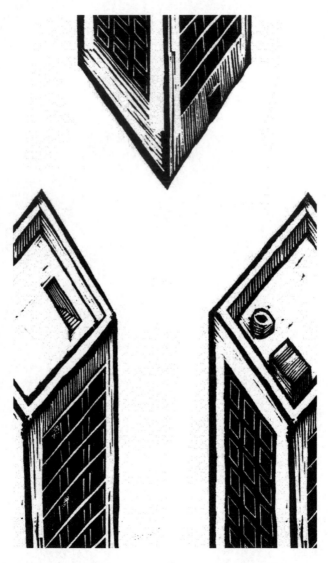

LOVE SONGS IN THE KEY OF Y

1. YANGTZE RIVER YODELLING SONG

We'll do yoga in a yurt,
we'll eat yogurt with a spoon
  then we'll backpack
  down the yak-track
  playing ukelele
  gaily
and we'll yodel to the yellow egg-yolk moon
  yodelay-di-he
  yo-ho-ho yoo-hoo
  yodel-(far away and fading
  into years ago and yonder)
   — you? who?

2. X + Y = ?

I txt my X.
  I asked her Y.
Y not, she said.
  Yes but, said I.

And yet, she said.
  What can I do,

I said. She said,
        If I were U

I'd press Erase.
        I pressed Resend.
Whichever way
        it spelled the end.

2 late 2 say
        we'd compromise
if I were U
        and we were Ys.

3. BYGONE GUY GOES ON (AND ON)

Oh I could have said Yes to Yolande,
I could have said Yes to Yvonne
        but now I'm left yearning,
        I'm yesterday's man.
You must say Yes today or it's gone.

I said Maybe to Maisie on Monday,
on Wednesday told Wendy to wait
        and said Just have to see
        now to Tina and Mina.

They did and they saw
that I'm just a has-been.
It's so early to find it's too late.

I was late being born as a baby.
I just couldn't make up my mind.
A yes-man I'm not,
I thought, laid in my cot.
I'll sit on the fence
through all life's events.
I'll hedge every bet
and I'll play hard to get.
(And did I get got?
No chance. I was not.)
If you can't say OK
to tomorrow today
even yesterday leaves you behind.

Oh I could have said Yes to Yolande,
I could have said Yes to Yvonne
Now I'm yearning and yawning,
I'm yesterday's man.
You must say Yes today or it's gone.

SAYING WHEN

I.

... One raindrop hit the pavement,
    then ten,
    then a million.
Ask him, ask her, they'll remember.

    That was when

the gutters were hissing, frills
    and spills
    tripping over
their feet in their rush to the sea.

    That was when

the green-tasting tang
    of wild garlic
    rose around them
freshly rinsed and shaken.

    That was when

they turned, first time in love
    with everything
    smoky and glittering,
seconds threaded like beads
    on the strings of the rain

which snapped. They were scattered.
      See him, see her,
      later, thinking *Yes,*
yes, that must have been when.

2.

. . . a jostle in the precinct,
      nothing special,
      was it? except maybe
the scrum was too tight and still . . .

      That was when

one stray laugh — a girl's
      or a boy's, shrill
      on something —
cut through, out of key.

      Was that it, then,

as the ones on the outside
      went on straining
      forward, the ones in
backed out, elbowing through

      or was that when

it was too late already?
      As they scattered,
      the flash of a knife . . .
and one just went on falling

      again and again

in my mind's eye, as I try
      to remember: was
      there a moment
somebody could have said *when*?

SHORT EXPOSURES

MACAQUE

Quick!
tracks his leap
as the world blurs.
Only he's in focus — him
and in the space
he's just left,
the rifle's
crack.

GRIZZLY

Up-
wind, nose
lifted, sniffing, dim
eyes bothering the blur
that's you ... Slow now, don't
run, back very *slowly*
off for seconds
that last
years.

HATCHING TURTLE

Go!
And time
begins. The moon
is a stopwatch, ticking.
No-one has told him anything.
All he knows, his legs paddling
dry sand on the wide
bare beach, is something
somewhere loves him
— call it
'sea'.

FIRE SAYS

We feed as we dance and we dance as we eat
fingerlicking flames and crunching feet
brushwood   buildings   everything we meet
all the same to the flame as we dance as we eat

Flint strike flint   and bone strike bone
Grandma Grandad Grinding Stone
bright spark leapt up lean and lone
went running through the wood like bone strike bone

Feed us   need us   slash and burn
whip the world like a top and make it turn
grassland jungle moss and fern
go up in smoke as we slash and burn

Wish and want   the dance of fire
willing whirling heart's desire
flirt and flare round the funeral pyre
you'll dance till you drop
        dance till you drop
          dance till you drop in the dance
                of fire

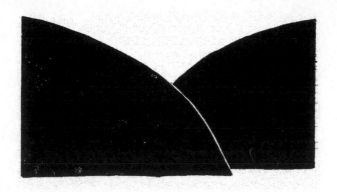

STONE SAYS

Once I was no-face,
a part of the heart of the hill.
Now we meet eye to eye —
a thing called me, a thing called you.

What news?
There was a time
you please to call the Stone Age.
I caught it in passing, just a blink ago.

But before that ... ?
Grindings of the star machine
for ever. Ever. Do you dare imagine?
That's why you need me,

to bear the weight
of all that time — me,
bedrock, hardcore, plinth,
foundation stone.

What can you tell me?
You, a flicker in the sunlight's eye,
what can you possibly know
that I don't? Yet ... I can feel

it in your step, you do.
Say something, quickly.
We have just this moment.
I don't want to go

on down the road,
the end-
less road
alone.

THE LIVING ROOM

I looked round the room. It was empty.
. . . . Nothing. Nobody at home —
    like a wet afternoon
    or a song with no tune,
       like a shrivelled balloon
       or a week on the moon.
And yet . . . no, I wasn't alone.

It may be the way things were standing,
how the floor creaked its one wonky board,
    or the curious feeling
    that up on the ceiling
       I heard a small voice
       from the paint that was peeling
say *Nothing likes being ignored.*

It said *Everything wants to be something.*
The bracket that once held a shelf —
    just one of it,
    blatantly one of a pair,
       now useless and loose
       but mysteriously *there* —
whispered: *Thanks, I can speak for myself.*

Because nothing is ever quite silent.
You've just never listened before.

The grate of the stool
that you pull up to sit
        says *I'm not a thing.*
        I'm a Me, not an It.
And who ever thinks of the floor?

Everything wants to be something.
Nothing likes being ignored.
        The butter knife
        in the back of the drawer
                that hasn't been used
                since the Second World War
still dreams it's a samurai sword.

And nothing's too dull to be mentioned
And nothing's too worn out to care.
        It may be hard
        and scuffed and scarred
                but the big old baggy-
                robed bum of a bard
once sat in this battered old chair.

And *Scratch me!* whispers the paper.
I've got secrets I don't want to hide.
        Depend on me,
        says the rusty old hook.

The window says *Look!*
(and so does the book).
there's a whole wide world outside.

And the put-upon lumpy-stuffed sofa
keeps history deep in its cracks —
     like a crossword, half done,
      and a pink plastic gun
        and a lottery ticket
        that just might have won
          and a raisin or two
        from a ten-year-old bun
and other mouth-watering snacks.

Because everything wants to be something
and everywhere could be explored.
    That small speck of mould
    has a tale to unfold
      about what it's like
      being lonely and old
    and the 100 watt light
    might look happy and bright
      but it may be afraid
      to be switched off at night
    and the phone in the hall
    has a friend it can't call

but nothing at all,
be it huge, be it small,
nothing likes being ignored.

IN EVERY ROOM THERE IS ONE
(But You Haven't Noticed Yet)

I'm a spidery
            crack
        working out
                from the corner
        of the ceiling
        so slowly
    that no human
            eye can see.

        Are you ready?

        Then I'll begin

        inch by inch
        setting out
    towards somewhere
        but
            where?
                until suddenly
    crash!

    and I'll let the sky in.

BY GUM

Dust . . . fluff . . . random stuff —
 whatever touches me, I cling.
Call me Sticky Nicky, call me Bob the Blob.
Don't blame me: it's just my job.
  I'll stick to anything.

Chair . . . desk . . . pavement . . . floor —
  when you don't look, I'm here.
Call me Dunc the Gunk or call me Sue the Goo.
Beneath your shoe, I'm there for you.
  You name it, I'll adhere.

Despised . . . displaced . . . once I had taste.
  I'm grey, downtrodden, old.
Call me what you like, my friend.
I'm with you till the sticky End,
  as close as your own sole.

MORE LUGGAGE FROM THE LOST AND FOUND

Item: a pod of titanium steel
scorched by re-entry to the stratosphere,
scratched by asteroid-grit like cat's claws,
and still cooling, not safe to touch.
Inside . . .

> a message from my dad the astronaut
> in orbit around Neptune's furthest moon
> saying *Miss You*, and a drop of zero gravity.
> For a moment I can't tell up from down.

~

Item: a parcel wrapped in bows and lace,
pink glitter-paper crimped as neat
as starched sheets with hospital corners,
like a professional smile. I rattle it, hard.
Inside . . .

> a hollow tinkle, rising, quickening,
> like one last coin in the slot machine
> or a gold ring, dropped and rolling
> on the pavement, near the open drain.

~

Item: a box that's not a box at all
but the *idea* of one — three dimensions,
East/West, North/South, High/Low. Now,
says the instruction, stretch them till they click.
Inside . . .

    is, suddenly, the room, the house,
    the town, the world; is you and me
    and the universe, tucked in snug, but for
    the nagging question: Where could *Outside* be?

IN PERSPECTIVE

A crooked door
hung in its frame
          askew . . .
Is it warped timbers or
the light? Something isn't
          quite true,

the way it opens not
quite at the angle
          you'd expect
to a long slanting hall
where light and shadows
          intersect

not right: the ceiling
and the floor converge
          too soon.
If parallel lines meet
at infinity, infinity is
          in this room

and crouched in the far
but strangely near distance
          is a man
who cries *Turn back*

or you'll end up the way
*   I am —*

a giant, crushed;
and I was once as straight
*   and neat as you.*
I left him there. The door
was open but he couldn't leave
    his point of view.

A SPIDER IN
GRANDFATHER'S SHED

No one knows how the world
  of the empty tea cup came
    into being. It may be
that the Great Gardener
    planned all the works of his hands
      to spread out in spiralling paths
      like galaxies

around this shed, this dark,
    this moon-white
      plastic picnic table
brought in for the winter,
    waiting for him (spring
      has come and gone),
      this small world,

chipped, earth-coloured
    with a dried-out stain,
    dark matter, and
suspended on my single thread
    of cobweb, lip to lip,
      above the emptiness,
      the fact of *me*

the storm's eye, me,
    the epicentre, me
        the point,
the very full stop
    of creation. Why else
        would all this
            have come to be?

IN THE LOST GARDEN

At some point
  on a walk
between whether
  and where

it stopped us
  with a quick
dry drip,
  the tap-tip

of palm fronds
  like impatient fingers
as if time
  was in a hurry to get on.

Somewhere
  a bumble hummed
like a motor left running
  on a ticking meter.

No one moved.
  The path had come,
like us, to no conclusion
  but half turned,

looking round
for something
or for someone
not quite here.

Like it, we hesitated
for about a hundred years

then we blinked and moved on.

SHADOW PARTY

Folded like the wings of old-gold birds,
the Chinese screens ... The hard green flames
of house plant in the fireplace ... Blinds
at half mast. Today, parlour games.

A writing desk sits in an alcove
like a darkened stage, with velvet swags and frills
heavily parted. Small pots of invisible ink.
Like flightless birds, the unused quills.

Thank you for not wearing stilettos /
taking photos. Red rope, gold-look poles, such
gracious forbiddings. And more *Thanks*
for not ... in German, French and Dutch.

An angel with unserviceable wings
and slender lily, in the servants' prayer room.
And books: 'The Daily Round', 'Ungilded Gold'
and simply 'Hymns With Tunes.'

Whose brush and hand-glass, silver-
backed with mermaids, whose face in it, whose
the candelabra'd dressing mirror, tiny
smoke-grey satin shoes?

At each turn of the stairs, the eyes,
the sad, heavy eyes. The youngest, precious two,
Victor and Violet, in skirts, gazing out as if
already lost, as if they knew.

A shadow party in a shut room.
Shrouded chairs. *Today is a light-saving day.*
The silver tea set glints. We're not invited, not
among them yet. We look away.

Lanhydrock House

TIDE RISING NEAR TINTAGEL

stone

flat black
stone

water folding over
flat black
stone

trampling on its backwash
water folding over
flat black
stone

crowd roar and crash   hush
trampling on its backwash
water folding over
flat black
stone

                              stone
                           flat black
                    water folding over
                 trampling on its backwash
              crowd roar and crash   hush

(I   came   here   to   be   alone)

RAIN IN THE RHONDDA

Cloud like the mountains closing over.
Thunder thumps on the lid of the day.
Listen to the Law that needs no preacher.
Water knows   knows how to fall.

Chains of rainfall, pump and piston,
clanking wheels of the hills' machine.
What's it for, this heavy labour?
Rain says nothing   knows it all.

Schoolyard, graveyard, chapel, boozer
wake up blinking from a dream of coal.
Soothe the slag hills, green-grassed over.
Water knows   knows how to fall.

Something flooded, drowned some, saved some.
A river of lives that's turned to stone,
a ten mile street that leads to nowhere.
Rain says nothing   knows it all.

Kingfisher flash and quick trout flicker.
No work's washed the river clean.
What will we do with this fruitless beauty?
Water knows   knows how to fall.

Rhondda flowing.
    Children growing.
Rain says nothing   knows it all.

BIG MUDDY BLUES

Tell me: what's my name? My name is Mud.
I'm bound to sing the blues 'cos muddy water's in my blood.
I'm the lowest of the low but you should see me when I flood.
    And you'd better just remember my name.

My daddy was the river. Mama was the deep red soil.
He was a travelling man. She was a daughter of toil.
But when they get together see those muddy waters boil
    and you'd better just remember my name.

The fine folk in white houses didn't like things getting brown.
They built levees and dug ditches to keep me out of town.
But on the day the rains come everyone must swim or drown
    and you'd better just remember my name.

There'll be weeping, there'll be wailing when the tide come in
    to stay.
There'll be mudslides in the mountains, there'll be roads
    washed clean away
but my name will still be Mud at the end of the day
    so you'd better just remember my name.

        And don't you forget it,
        any time you're feeling low:
        mud has been there, and been deeper.

Mud's been down
down
as far as you can go.

Sing it:
Go down Moses, go down muddy,
go down deep into the soul . . .

I just thought you ought to know.

THE OLD WIFE'S TALE

A story ... Once, before time could be told, in the heart of the forest, sat a witch. Not bad, not good — this was before good and bad were invented. She was just old.

She sat in a tree, in the crook of two branches, for so long the tree had grown round her, so she could not have got up and walked away even if she wanted. Which she did not. So she sat.

Beneath the tree was the path through the wood, and the wood was too thick to pass without a path and too wide to go round. And this was where she waited. So.

Some time after, a swarm of flies came by and the witch said: Halt. You may all pass but one, you leave me one, that's how it is. And the flies buzzed: Sure, take one, we're all the same. And a frog jumped out of the wood and gulp! had one, and the witch said: thank you, and the flies went on.

Some time after, the frog spawned and the tadpoles turned to little hoppers, hundreds of them on the forest path, and the witch said: Halt. All pass but one. And the frogs said: all the same to us, and the witch said: thank you, and a cat pounced from the bushes and played with one wounded frog for an hour, the way cats do, and all the rest hopped on.

Some time after, the cat had kittens and the farm folk said: Too many cats, throw them out in the forest. And when the kittens came to the tree on the path the witch said: Halt. And one kitten was so scared that she ran straight home, where the farm boys put her in a sack and drowned her in the frog pond. And the other cats went on.

Some time after again was a war, and people ran from the farm that was burning, and came down the path to the tree and the witch said: Halt. Which one of you is it to be?

But the people said: We are not flies or frogs or cats, we are people and we can't say: Yes, take one. But you must decide, said the witch. So the people sat down right there on the path and talked and argued and debated and made politics about it and took counsel. And night came, and rain fell, and it turned to snow and ice, so when the witch looked in the morning all of them had frozen there, dead on the path.

The witch wept when she saw it, great tears of amber sap oozed from her tree. But, she said, I only wanted one . . .

MY PLACE

Postcards from the State of Poetry

1.

A squat, a grand house
        fallen on hard times
with slates slipped from the roof
        and the rain coming in.

On the shut-shop windows
        and boarded-up door,
a *Notice To Evict* . . . But
        if you're very thin

you can prise back a plank
        and slip through
into darkness, a shuddering bass
        in your bones, a flame-flicker
        that ripples your skin,

and dancers, dancing
        till they drop . . .
and all the neighbours coming out
        like ghosts
        who can't sleep for the din.

2.
   An igloo
        on an ice floe,
the black-blue
        deep below . . .

You wake one morning
to feel everything gone queasy,
        swaying, shifting
on the currents that were always
just beneath your feet.

You're drifting south to the seas of the sun.

. . . the igloo
        and the ice floe
more brittle and see-through
        the further you go . . .

You lay down last night in a story.
Today it's grown thin and essential
        as a line of poetry,

a phrase that must be right,
a single word you have to utter

if it's the last thing you do. Yes, that one.

2b.
In another version
of the igloo story,
there's you
on the melting ice floe.

And the bear.

3.
  The Whispering Vault:

who knows how they raised it, this dome
in the desert, with not a tree in sight,
            not a stone?

Or why? But at each of the four
points of the compass rose, a doorway
            with no door

admits the winds. Faint voices blown

from each horizon enter, and they stay,
they whisper here — for years, for ever.
            Gone astray

on the journey you come on this empty
shell in the sand. You may find a voice
speaking. It may

speak to you. And it may be your own.

4.
    It might be a mineshaft
or a pothole where a river went to earth

and so you might,

where limestone has been carved by ancient water
into shapes like candle wax,

where green moss glows with its own light.

If you can hold your breath
you'll hear, not see, the cave-pool,

icy-night-sky-clear:

each drip after drip running back
beneath the world to meet its echo

back, back, as far as the human ear

or the tingle in your mind
can follow. *Hear*, it whispers.

Here. And *here*. And *here* . . .

5.
    An ancient city, half in ruins,
      with tents pitched in amongst the rubble

and stalls by the roadside,
      ragged children with their canny eyes

and a few words in your language: *Hey,*
      mister, lady, you want treasure?

selling what they've scavenged. One day
      it's a turquoise death-mask,

the next, a jewelled sun-disc of a DVD.

6.
A breath, that's all it is,
of other air

like the shade of a Bedouin tent,
cool drapes,

a smell of smoke and coffee.
Step in,

barefoot, from the desert glare
and speak,

though till your eyes accustom
you can't tell

who's waiting. All you have
is your voice in the dark,

and maybe there's nobody,
nothing; maybe

all the world is waiting there.

ROOM INSIDE

There's a room in my house where nobody goes
    except me:
a still room, a light room,
    a where-I-go-to-write room,
an any-day, any-time, a middle-of-the-night room,
    a feeling-low-and-slow or a high-as-a-kite room.
        Feel free!

There's a room in my house where nobody goes.
There are cupboards and corners that nobody knows
    inside me.

There's a room in my house where nobody has been
    except me:
a just-behind-your-face room,
    an orbiting-in-space room,
an earthquake-shaking-with-the-thumping-of-the-bass room,
    a somewhere-to-escape-to-outside-the-human-race room,
        a just-close-your-eyes-and-you'll-vanish-without-trace room
        suddenly.

There's a room in my house where nobody has been.
There's a view from my window nobody has seen
    inside me.

There are secret compartments that nobody's guessed
   except me:
a shadow room, a cool room,
  a chalky-smelling school room,
a kidney-shaped Hollywood parties-by-the-pool room,
  an old-French-blokes-in-berets-playing-boule room,
    a rusty-dusty buckets full of grandfather's tools room,
     a locked junk trunk that might be full of jewels room
      possibly.

There are secret compartments that nobody's guessed.
There's another direction than north/south/east/west
   inside me.

There's a room that is private, that no one can own.
   Come and see.
A music room, a dance room,
  a things-found-quite-by-chance room,
a jungle room, a tigers-in-amongst-the-potted-plants room,
  a hiding-from-a-hundred-jolly-uncles-and-strange-aunts
    room,
    no family . . .
An X marks the spot room,
  a don't ask why, why-not room,
a sauna-in-the-winter-and-a-freezer-when-it's-hot room,
  a sail-to-the-horizon-in-a-little-tin-pot-yacht room

with its own sea.
A cellar room, an attic room,
    a semi-automatic room,
a can't-sit-still-cos-I'm-crackling-with-static room,
        a much-too-emphatic sort of amateur-dramatic room —
oh, tragedy!

There's a room that is private, that no one can own.
You can build one yourself out of breath, flesh and bone.
    There's a padlock that opens to nobody's key.
Just knock,
        and wait,
            and knock,
                and wait,
and when a voice says 'Who's there?'
                say, 'Just me.'

A NOTE ON
THE ILLUSTRATIONS
Jonathan Gross

These pictures were engraved on vinyl floor-tiles,
inked with a roller, and relief-printed onto smooth
Zerkall paper.

The greatest challenge of producing illustrations for
this book was to try not to duplicate the imagery
already vivid in the words, but to find instead an
interesting visual tangent to explore.

http://www.engrossing.co.uk/